THE MUNSTERS JOKE BOOK

Ever heard Herman's howlers or suffered from eerie ache?

Have you got the party spirit or are you just dead romantic?

Well, welcome to a Munster of a joke book. It's guaranteed to have you shrieking with laughter!

Other Knight Books you will enjoy:

THE INTER GALACTIC JOKE BOOK
Ann Droid

SOGGY SEMOLINA – THE SCHOOL DINNERS JOKE BOOK
Egon Chips

HOW TO HALT A HICCUP AND OTHER HANDY HINTS
Mary Danby

SURVIVAL! A SCHOOL KID'S GUIDE
Gladys Over

THE MUNSTERS JOKE BOOK

by Bea Warned

Illustrated by Jean Baylis

KNIGHT BOOKS
Hodder and Stoughton

First published in Great Britain in 1990 by Knight Books

British Library C.I.P.

Warned, Bea
The Munsters joke book.
1. Children's humour in English, 1945–
I. Title II. Baylis, Jean
827.914

ISBN 0-340-53841-4

Typeset by Rowland Phototypesetting Ltd., Bury St Edmunds, Suffolk. Printed and bound in Great Britain for Hodder and Stoughton Children's Books, a division of Hodder and Stoughton Ltd., Mill Road, Dunton Green, Sevenoaks, Kent TN13 2YA. (Editorial Office: 47 Bedford Square, London WC1B 3DP) by Cox and Wyman Ltd., Reading, Berks.

What do you call Herman when he's in a bad mood?
Anything he wants you to.

Why is Herman so funny?
Because he soon has you in stitches.

Did you hear what Herman bought Lily for her birthday?
A demon necklace – after all, demons are a ghoul's best friend.

Where did Herman stay when he went on a business trip?
In a ghost-house.

What did Lily say to Herman when he was ill?
'Herman, what's happened to your spirit?'

Did Herman tell you about his friend with the glass eye?
It usually comes out in conversation.

What does Herman wear when he goes fishing?
Ghouloshes.

HERMAN: I want to buy your mother a dress to match her eyes.
MARILYN: Daddy, how romantic!
HERMAN: Yes, but where will I find one that's bloodshot?

HERMAN: I'm so mad my blood's boiling.
GRANDPA: Now, now Herman. Simmer down.

Herman doesn't go to a tailor. He wears ready-to-werewolf suits.

What do you do if Herman knocks at your door?
Hide!

HERMAN: Aaaagh, Lily! What's that hideous thing on your shoulders?
LILY: Yuck, get it off quickly.
HERMAN: Sorry, darling. It was only your head.

Herman always takes a while to clean his teeth. He likes to gargoyle afterwards.

Herman doesn't like going back to work after the weekend. He always loathed Moandays.

Herman wanted to go to sea when he was younger. But the only job they would offer him was ghost guard.

Herman used to be very handsome – until he gruesome whiskers.

What should you do when Herman sneezes?
Run for cover.

Did you notice how straight Herman's back is? He always sits bolt upright.

LILY: Herman dear, how did you get that splinter in your finger?
HERMAN: Oh, I just scratched my head.

What did Herman's left ear say to the right ear?
"I didn't know we were living on the same block."

What happens when you turn Herman upside down?
His nose runs and his feet smell.

LILY: Eeek! Herman – there are three left hands, two knees and a right foot in the fridge!
HERMAN: I know dear – they're spare parts.

HERMAN: Eddie, I thought I'd take you to the zoo today.
EDDIE: Dad, if the zoo wants me they can come and get me.

HERMAN: My father once faced a hairy ape in the jungle and never turned a hair.
LILY: That's not very surprising, dear – your father was bald.

HERMAN: I slept like a log last night.
LILY: I know dear, I heard you sawing it.

HERMAN: The bus conductor told me I couldn't stand on the top deck.
LILY: Why ever not dear?
HERMAN: It was only a single decker.

What did Herman's left eye say to his right eye?
"Between you and me, something here smells."

EDDIE: Dad, are you as tough as you look?
HERMAN: I chew nails.
EDDIE: Brass or steel ones?
HERMAN: Finger.

LILY: Herman, put the kettle on for me.
HERMAN: But why dear? It will be much too small for me.

When Herman was younger they said he had a photographic mind.
It's a shame it never developed.

HERMAN: There weren't many of us at work today.
LILY: Weren't there dear?
HERMAN: No, we were working with a skeleton crew.

Why is Herman never lonely?
Because he is so good at making friends.

Herman doesn't like the story of King Kong. In fact, he dislikes it so much, he thinks it's ape-alling.

What do you call it when Herman turns green?
The Incredible Sulk.

How do you stop Herman from smelling?
Cut off his nose.

What kind of shoe does Herman wear?
Incredibly large ones – so large that they're munstrous!

HERMAN: My late uncle was a mathematician.
EDDIE: Oh really? But why did he die?
HERMAN: Oh – his number came up.

LILY: What are you reading dear?
HERMAN: *Ghoulliver's Travels.*

HERMAN: Grandpa's bat isn't very well.
EDDIE: Perhaps its battery has run out.

How does Herman count to a hundred?
On his fingers.

Pretty Ugly

Did you hear what happened when Lily went to the beauty parlour for a facelift?
They subcontracted the work to the local builders.

What do you call a Munster with nine eyes, twelve arms, four noses and twenty legs?
Extremely handsome.

Why are vampires like false teeth?
They both come out at night.

Did you know that when Marilyn grows up she wants to be a model?
She hopes to be a cover ghoul.

What do you call a Munster with four heads, six arms and ten legs?
Anything he wants you to!

Where does Lily Munster have her hair done?
At the Ugly Parlour.

Did you hear what happened when Lily entered the beauty contest?
Nobody won.

Grandpa says that Lily was a pretty baby. Yes, she was indeed. Pretty ugly.

Eddie was such an ugly baby that Lily didn't push him in the pram – she pulled him.

LILY: Marilyn, eat up your greens – they're good for your complexion.
MARILYN: But I don't want a green complexion.

LILY: Is there anything different about the new girl in your class?
MARILYN: There certainly is – she's got a beard.

EDDIE: Mother, the boys at school say I look like a werewolf.
LILY: Oh, do be quiet and comb your face.

Did you hear about the Munster with pedestrian eyes? They look each way before they cross.

EDDIE: Mother, why do you put all that powder on your face?
LILY: To make me look more beautiful dear.
EDDIE: When does it start to work?

Did you hear about Herman before he met Lily? He was so ugly he had to go out with a prune because he couldn't get a date.

HERMAN: You know dear, Marilyn has silken hair, beautiful eyes and skin like a peach.
LILY: I know – she's so ugly.

MARILYN: That new pop singer's so handsome.
LILY: Yes. I bet he gets a lot of fang mail.

HERMAN: Why don't you ever put cream on your face, dear?
LILY: Because whenever I put it on it curdles.

Munster Munchies

EDDIE: Mum, I don't like Auntie Doreen.
LILY: Shut up and just eat your beans then.

What do the Munsters eat in winter?
Ghoulash.

What do the Munsters eat for breakfast?
Dreaded Wheat.

What is Eddie's favourite treat?
I-scream!

What does Herman pour on his Sunday lunch?
Grave-y.

What's Herman's favourite snack?
Monster Munch.

What is Herman's favourite breakfast cereal?
Ready Neck.

What do the Munsters drink out of?
Cups and sorcerers.

What is Lily Munster's favourite soup?
Scream of tomato.

What is Marilyn's favourite fruit?
Blood oranges.

What is Grandpa's favourite fruit?
Necktarines.

What did Lily say when she came back from the supermarket?
'I'm so tired, I'm dead on my feet.'

What do you call a drunken ghost?
A methylated spirit.

Do you know what Herman's German relatives drink beer from?
Frankensteins.

What is Grandpa's favourite snack?
Fang-furters.

LILY: How would you like your eggs dear?
HERMAN: Terror-fried.

EDDIE: This stew is delicious, Mum.
LILY: Thank you Eddie but stop goblin your food down.

EDDIE: What are the best things to put into cake?
GRANDPA: Teeth.

EDDIE: Mum. may I leave the table?
LILY: Well, you certainly can't take it with you!

What's Grandpa's favourite drink?
Quick Brew.

What's Eddie's favourite drink?
Demon-ade.

LILY: Eddie we've got some guests coming to lunch. Go and clean yourself up.
EDDIE: Why Mum? They're not going to eat me are they?

LILY: Herman, what happened to all those cakes I baked? I told you you couldn't have one and now there's only one left.
HERMAN: I know – that's the one you said I couldn't have.

LILY TO MARILYN: Stop daydreaming and drink your soup before it clots.

GRANDPA: Lily, there's a frog in my soup.
LILY: Yes, the fly is on holiday.

HERMAN: Lily, there's a fly in my soup.
LILY: Yes, it's the rotting meat that attracts them.

HERMAN: How many people are we having for dinner, dear?
LILY: Oh, just one each.

What do the Munsters drink in summer?
Ice-ghouled drinks.

What kind of crockery do the Munsters have?
Bone china.

What's Lily's favourite tea-time treat?
Devil's food cake.

HERMAN: I'm sorry I'm late for dinner, dear.
LILY: You should be, everyone's eaten.

FOR SALE: TEAK COFFIN
ONE PREVIOUS OWNER ALSO -
SHROUD - ONLY WORN ONCE
WILL CONSIDER PART-EXCHANGE
CALL - S. POOKY

NEED H
LIKE A
Call: DE

LOST - LEF
If found pleas
to Second-H

LOST
FAMILY PET
GREEN WITH YELLOW SCALES
FRIENDLY - AFFECTIONATE
ANSWERS TO NAME OF
SPOTTY
BREATHES FIRE WHEN
HUNGRY — HAS BATTLE-AXE SCAR
ON LEFT SHOULDER...

WEREWO
FOR ALL YOU
We can
beetles
vultu
and

NEED A CARPENTER?
Call WOODY. Trapdoors
Coffins and Dragon runs
a speciality - Toadstools
made to order...

MUNSTER
ADVERTISEMENTS

?? LIFE SEEM
IOUS CIRCLE ?
ON AID

HAND
return
d Shop...

SKELETON KEYS
CUT WHILE U WAIT
STAKES ALSO SHARPENED

VAMPIRES!
Contact the Consumer
Association with all
those nibbling problems.
THE ORGANISATION WITH THE
HUMAN TOUCH!

ES
S' NEEDS
r slugs
ffon
maggots
eevils...

TOOTH ACHE ?
CONTACT Count Dracula 666

Lily's Laughs

Do you know Lily's secret?
She's got a skeleton in her cupboard.

How does Lily tell the time?
By her witch-watch.

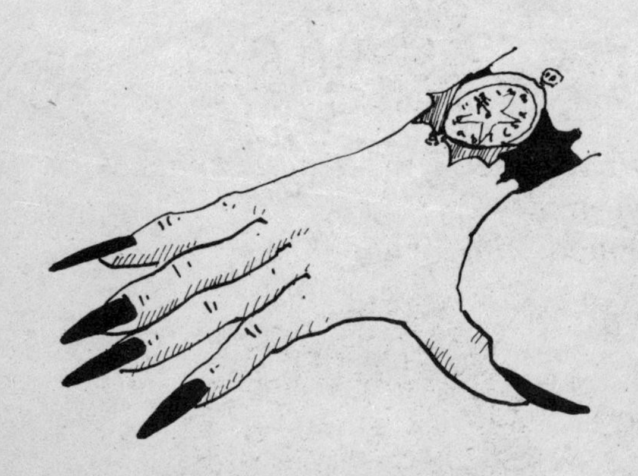

What did Lily say to Eddie?
'Don't spook until you are spooken to!'

Lily loves music. Her favourite tunes are haunting melodies . . .

What do you call it when Lily makes a mistake?
A booooo-booooo!

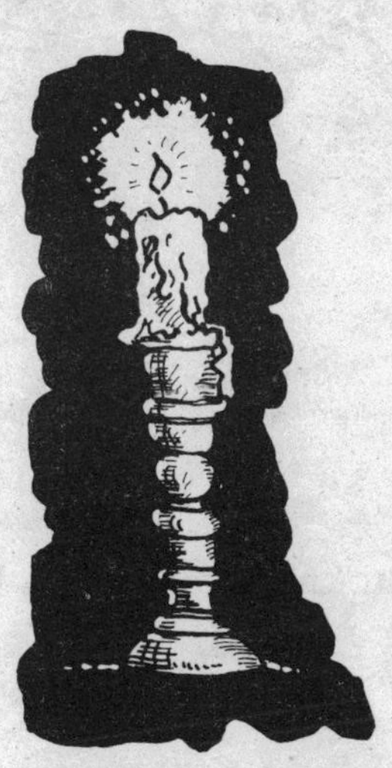

What noise do the Munsters make when they cry?
Booooo-hoooooooooo!

Who brings Munster babies?
Frankenstork.

Did you know that Lily's friend is writing a book?
She's a ghost writer.

LILY: Herman, did you remember to put the cat out?
HERMAN: I didn't know it was on fire, dear.

LILY'S FIRST FRIEND: Did you hear about the time Lily went to Switzerland? She came back with a clock.
LILY'S SECOND FRIEND: A cuckoo clock?
LILY'S FIRST FRIEND: No – a buzzard clock.

LILY: Herman, thank goodness you're home, I've been waiting outside for ages.
HERMAN: But why didn't you go in, dear?
LILY: Because I've lost my skeleton key.

Where was Lily when the lights went out?
In the dark.

EDDIE: Mother, can I play with Grandpa?
LILY: No you can't – you've dug him up twice this week already.

What's Lily's favourite dance?
The Last Vaults.

LILY: Why are you looking at the mirror with your eyes shut, dear?
HERMAN: I want to see what I look like when I'm asleep.

Did you hear that Lily bought Herman some aftershave for his birthday?
It was called Brut.

Lily's sister is getting married – she's entering Holy Dreadlock.

Lily was thinking of getting a job – as a demon-strator.

Did you know that Lily wears toilet water? It comes from her own toilet.

Lily never uses the lift in department stores. She prefers to use the scares.

Lily loves going to street markets. She's very good at haggling.

LILY: Was Grandpa's joke funny dear?
HERMAN: Funny? It was hellarious.

HERMAN: Lily, why are you so worried.
LILY: I'm not sure that Marilyn's new boyfriend is the right boy for her.
HERMAN: Don't worry, dear, it will all work out. After all, every shroud has a silver lining.

LILY: Goodness me, it's cold out there.
HERMAN: Is it?
LILY: It's so cold, I'm chilled to the bone.

HERMAN: Oh look, it's raining.
LILY: Oh no! I hate it when it rains. It really dampens the spirits.

GRANDPA: What are those charming plants in the garden?
LILY: Marighouls.

LILY: I never thought I'd calm that ghost down.
HERMAN: I knew you'd reach a happy medium.

1st FIEND: My cousin Vampire has written to say he'll be coming to stay next week.
2nd FIEND: Great. I'll dig a hole in the garden and ask him to drop in.

Did you know that the Munsters went on holiday? They went all over the country from ghost to ghost.

Where do the Munsters like to spend their holiday?
Lake Eerie.

How do the Munsters prefer to travel?
On fright trains.

Did you hear about the hotel the Munsters stayed in?
It was so bad, it was ghostly . . .

1st VAMPIRE: Fangs, how good to see you!
2nd VAMPIRE: Well, I was in the area so I thought I'd make a flying visit.

Lily's booked the Munsters' summer holiday. They are going to the Ghosta del Sol. Last year they went to Wails.

Once a year, the Munsters visit their relatives. They live a long way away, in another terrortory.

Do Munsters go on safaris?
Not safaris I know.

Eddie went on a school trip to France once. They flew to Charles de Ghoul airport.

Where do the Munsters go swimming?
The Dead Sea.

Did you know a Red Indian is coming to stay with the Munsters?
They are going to put him up in a Creepee.

What do the Munsters do when they go camping with Grandpa?
Sit around the vampire and howl!

Next year the Munsters are going to Scotland to stay with a relative – the Loch Ness Munster.

EDDIE: Gee Grandpa, I'm glad I wasn't born in France.
GRANDPA: Why?
EDDIE: I can't speak French.

THE MUNSTER LIBRARY

THE MUNSTERS BOOK OF HORROR STORIES
by TERRY FIE

THE DENTISTS HANDBOOK
BY COUNT DRACULA

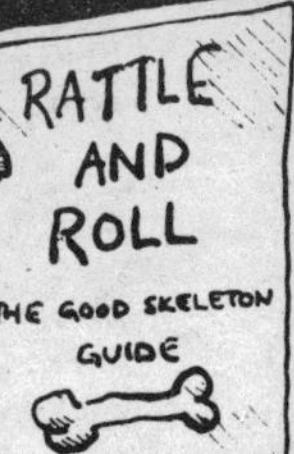
RATTLE AND ROLL
THE GOOD SKELETON GUIDE
by NORA BONE

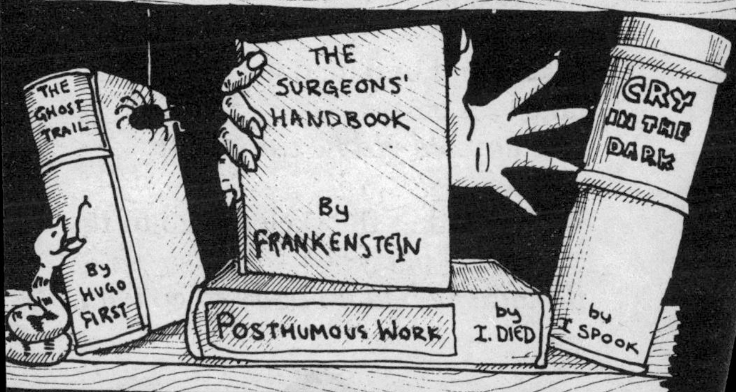
THE GHOST TRAIL
By HUGO FIRST
THE SURGEONS' HANDBOOK
By FRANKENSTEIN
CRY IN THE DARK
by I SPOOK
POSTHUMOUS WORK
by I. DIED

THE WITCH GUIDE TO Problem Solving
by ANNE GUISH
FIND YOUR OWN HUSBAND
by IDA DORA HUSBAND
ONE MAN'S BED IS ANOTHER MAN'S COFFIN!
The Book of MUNSTER PROVERBS
by ERN NEST
THE OFFALLY TASTY COOK BOOK
by LILY LIVERED
SCARE YOURSELF SILLY
by I. SCREAM

What did Grandpa say when he was given a birthday present?
'Fangs a lot!'

What kind of date does a Munster take to a party?
Oh, any old girl he can dig up.

Why couldn't the skeleton go to the Munsters' party?
Because he had no body to go with.

What do you call Eddie's birthday party?
A seance.

What do the Munsters play at parties?
Haunt and Spook.

Did you hear about the skeletons who went to the Munsters' party?
They had a rattling good time.

Do you know what the Munsters went to the fancy dress Hallowe'en party as?
Normal people.

EDDIE: I think that ghoul over there likes me. She just rolled her eyes at me.
HIS FRIEND: Well, roll them right back – she might need them.

Did you hear what drinks Herman served at the party?
Whines and spirits.

The Munsters are holding their next party on the top floor of a ten-storey building because the guests at their last party were in such high spirits.

Grandpa's Groaners

EDDIE: Grandpa, do fleas hibernate?
GRANDPA: Search me.

Did you hear about Grandpa's latest potion? It tasted awful.
Apparently he made a grave mistake . . .

Grandpa is always happy to chat to the neighbours. He likes to see new blood around.

Why did Grandpa eat flour and furniture polish?
Because he wanted to rise and shine.

Grandpa's going to enter a car race. He wants to win the Hearse of the Year Show.

What does Grandpa do each night at midnight?
He takes a coffin break.

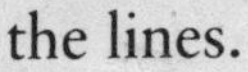

GRANDPA: Lily's really beautiful, isn't she?
HERMAN: Yes, if you read between the lines.

Did you hear that Grandpa wanted a pedigree dog?
He was thinking of buying a bloodhound.

Do you know what Grandpa's favourite hobbies are?
Haunting, shooting and fishing.

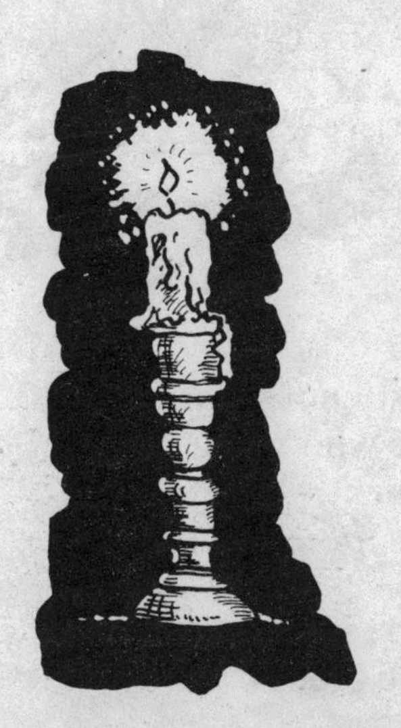

Why won't Grandpa eat in restaurants?
He doesn't want to get a steak in the heart.

What did Grandpa say to his friend as he waved him goodbye?
'It's been nice gnawing you.'

Did you know that Grandpa had a relative who was a Member of Parliament?
He was the Deputy Spooker.

Grandpa is very artistic. He's good at drawing blood.

Where does Grandpa keep his money?
At the bloodbank – although he hates to be bloodshot.

Grandpa used to be a boxer but he gave it up. He didn't want to spoil his looks. It was a shame really – he was Champion Phantom Weight.

Why is Grandpa so crazy?
Because he is often bats.

Grandpa tried to hail a cab the other day but he was accused of being an Inspectre of Taxis.

Did you hear about Grandpa's ghostly friend? He was arrested because he didn't have a haunting licence.

Grandpa used to be a very good cricketer.
He was always first bats-man.

Grandpa bought Herman and Lily towels for their anniversary.
They've got 'his' and 'hearse' embroidered on them.

Grandpa's thinking of working in television as a crypt writer.

EDDIE: Grandpa, don't drive so fast – it's terrifying.
GRANDPA: Do what I do, Eddie – close your eyes.

MARILYN: Grandpa, you're such a smart dresser.
GRANDPA: I know. I always dress to kill.

What do you call it when the Munsters have something to celebrate?
A Dead Letter Day.

Grandpa loves dancing – especially the fangdango!

MARILYN: The cellar walls are covered in spots, Mother. I suppose they are from Grandpa's experiments?
LILY: No dear, his latest experiment went wrong. They are Grandpa.

MARILYN: Grandpa, who's your favourite composer?
GRANDPA: Bathoven.

Grandpa used to be able to run really fast when he was younger. He was neck and neck with someone once in a race. But then he overtook them with breakneck speed.

GRANDPA: Herman, that was a lovely necklace you bought Lily.
HERMAN: That wasn't a necklace. That was a choker.

If Grandpa has fangs, does that mean he uses fang paste?

Grandpa's really clever – he's a Batchelor of Arts.

ART FANGNATIC: Who's that incredible painting by?
GRANDPA: Oh, my cousin Vincent, Vincent Van Ghost.

It took Grandpa a long time to get his latest experiment right. It was a case of trial and terror.

Why did Herman go to the hospital?
To have his ghoul stones removed.

LILY: Did you know that Herman is ill?
GRANDPA: No, what's wrong with him?
LILY: He's suffering from a pain in the neck.

LILY: Doctor, Herman's much better. He's not feeling so drained.
DOCTOR: I told you that a good rest would help him.
LILY: No doctor, it wasn't that. He got struck by lightning.

What noise do Munsters make when they are feeling ill?
Groan.

Did you hear that Marilyn wants to be a nurse? She's been practising bandaging at the British Museum.

EDDIE (to his best friend): I used to be a werewolf, but I'm all right nooooooooooooooowooooooooh!

Do you know how Herman keeps so fit?
He takes plenty of exorcise.

What noise does Grandpa make when he's got toothache?
Chomp, chomp, suck – ouch!

What did the dentist say to Grandpa?
'Phew! You've got bat breath!'

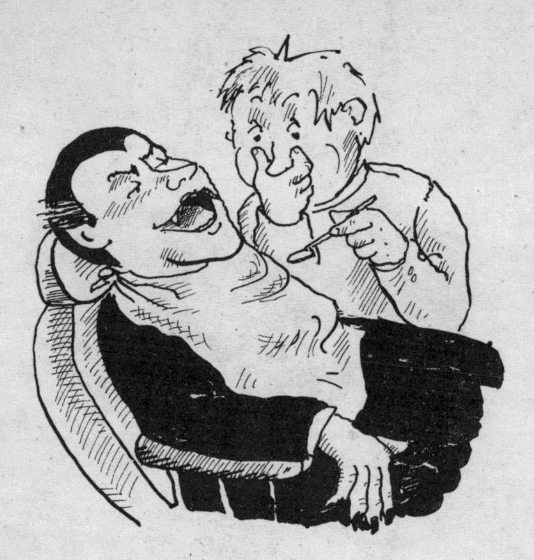

GRANDPA: Doctor, I'm having trouble with my breathing.
DOCTOR FANG: Oh well, we'll have to put a stop to that.

Did you hear about the Munster with a bad ear?
He had eerie ache . . .

HERMAN: I feel really terrible Doctor. I think I'm at death's door.
DOCTOR: Don't worry. I'll pull you through.

Why was Grandpa so ill?
Because of his coffin.

Why did Grandpa jump up and down?
Because he forgot to shake the bottle before he took his coffin mixture.

What do you do when a Munster turns blue?
Cheer him up.

LILY: I don't seem to be able to see very well these days.
HERMAN: You'd better go to the optician, dear, you might need to wear spooktacles.

Which Munster has the best hearing?
The eeriest.

LILY: Herman, why have you tied a knot in your neck?
HERMAN: Well dear, I didn't want my cold to go to my chest.

DOCTOR: I'm sorry sir, but I don't like the look of your wife.
HERMAN: Don't worry, I haven't liked the look of her for years.

DOCTOR: I'm sorry, your father has rigor mortis.
LILY: What does that mean, doctor? Is it serious?
DOCTOR: Well, let's just say that he'll be a little stiff in the morning.

HERMAN: Grandpa, how can I stop my nose from running?
GRANDPA: Put your foot out and trip it up.

Did you hear about Lily's girlfriend? She's going to hospital to have an apparition.

GRANDPA: The first time the doctor looked at my tonsils he said, 'My boy, you will carry those tonsils with you to your grave.' And he was right, I've done it many times.

HERMAN: For goodness sake Eddie! I know you're ill but do stop moaning about it.
EDDIE: Is there anywhere in this house where I can find any sympathy?
HERMAN: Yes – the dictionary.

Grandpa saw a funeral procession and asked someone who had died.
'The woman in the coffin of course!'

Marilyn's boyfriend's parents are zombies. He calls them Mummy and Dead.

Did you hear that Marilyn learnt to ride a horse? It was a nightmare.

Marilyn's boyfriend's mummy has never had a cold. She's always well wrapped up.

MARILYN: Eddie, your friends are weird.
EDDIE: Why, what's wrong with them?
MARILYN: They're all bats.

Marilyn was engaged to a man with a wooden leg but she broke it off.

What's the name of Marilyn's favourite rock band?
The blood group.

Marilyn's Egyptian friend's mummy can always keep a secret. She's good at keeping things under wraps.

MARILYN: Mother, a salesman has just tricked Grandpa out of £100.
LILY: Well dear, he always was a real sucker.

Marilyn's got a new boyfriend. He's really gruesome.

MARILYN: Mother, Daddy's acting really strangely.
LILY: Don't worry, he's probably got a screw loose.

Herman's favourite television programme is *Horrornation Street*. Marilyn prefers *Neighbooooos*!

What is Marilyn's favourite story?
Ghouldilocks and the three bears.

Why was Marilyn's Egyptian friend worried?
Because her Daddy was a mummy.

MARILYN: You know that vase that's been handed from generation to generation?
LILY: Yes dear?
MARILYN: Well, this generation's dropped it.

LILY: Is Marilyn's boyfriend coming round after tea again?
HERMAN: That's all he does come round for.

Marilyn's got a friend who's a ghost. Her mum and dad are transparents.

Why did Marilyn's boyfriend take her to see a horror movie?
Because they love each shudder of course.

What did Marilyn say to her new vampire boyfriend?
'You're beginning to get under my skin.'

GRANDPA: I had a girlfriend once who had an identical twin sister.
MARILYN: How could you tell them apart?
GRANDPA: Simple – my girlfriend was the one with the beard.

Herman's Headlines
SKELETON GIVES UP HOPE
Heart isn't in it
WATCH DOG STARTS TO TICK
CHARLES DE GHOUL AIRPORT HAUNTED
ABOMINABLE SNOWMAN EATS CHILE AND BLOWS HIS COOL
'Toad-in-the-hole' voted best dish by Witch Guide
FROZEN SKELETON FOUND
Is he a numbskull?

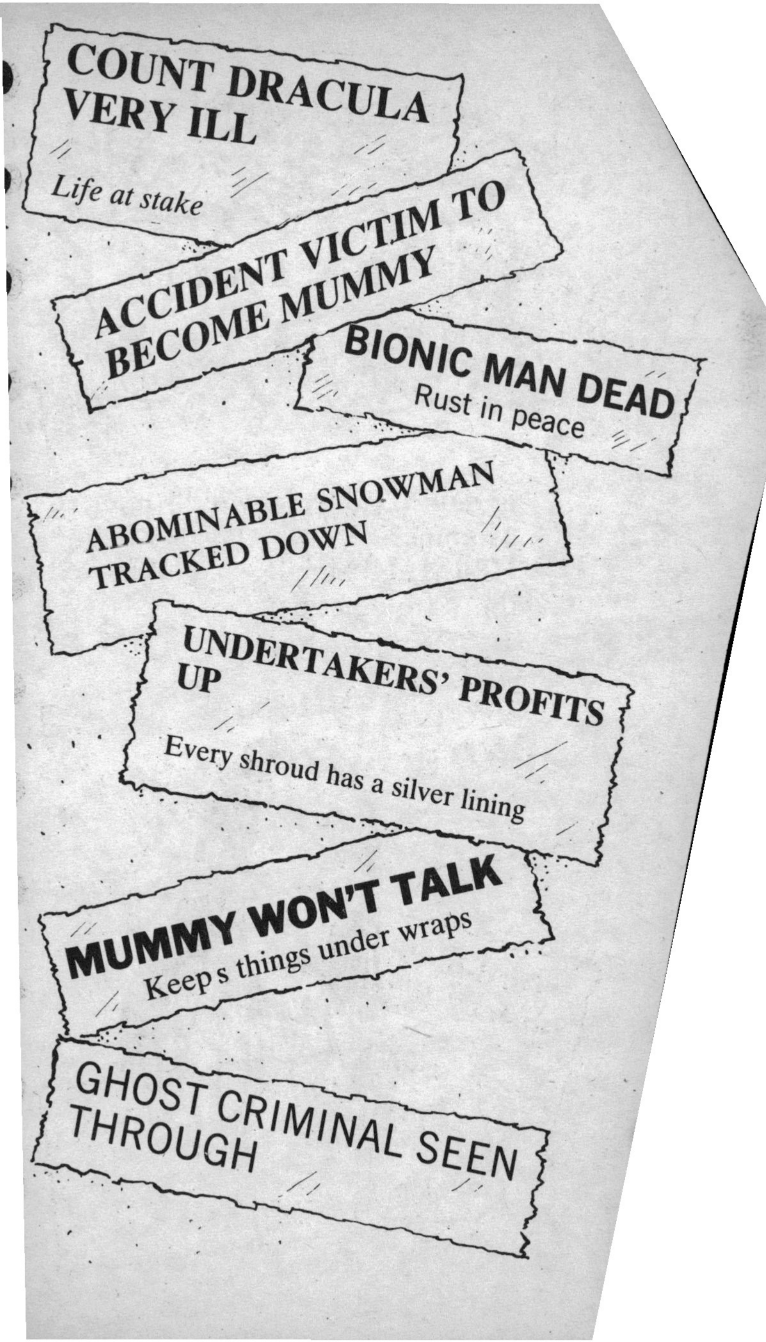
COUNT DRACULA VERY ILL
Life at stake
ACCIDENT VICTIM TO BECOME MUMMY
BIONIC MAN DEAD
Rust in peace
ABOMINABLE SNOWMAN TRACKED DOWN
UNDERTAKERS' PROFITS UP
Every shroud has a silver lining
MUMMY WON'T TALK
Keep s things under wraps
GHOST CRIMINAL SEEN THROUGH

Dead Romantic

EDDIE: Daddy, how did you meet Mummy?
HERMAN: Simple, son, I removed a thorn from her paw.

Did you know where Lily and Herman got married?
Westmunster Abbey . . .

. . . And did you hear about the engagement ring that Herman bought?
It was a tombstone.

Why didn't Grandpa's brother get married?
Because he was a bat-chelor.

LILY: Herman, will you love me even when I'm wrinkly and ugly?
HERMAN: But Lily, of course I do.

Why are the Munsters such a close family?
Because blood is thicker than water.

Why was Marilyn so upset?
Because she thought her romance with the vampire was in vein.
Her first boyfriend was a vampire as well – only he was a pain in the neck.

Did you hear that Herman is taking Lily to the theatre to celebrate their anniversary?
They're going to see *The Phantom of the Opera.*
Did you hear how much Lily enjoyed it?
She thought it was spooktacular.

When Grandpa married Lily's mother it was very romantic. He had fallen for the ghoul necks door.

MARILYN: Mother, when did you know that Daddy was the man for you?
LILY: Well darling, it was a case of love at first fright.

Marilyn's boyfriend is an Undertaker – he's embalmy about her.

LILY: Is it true you've fallen in love with a vampire?
MARILYN: Yes. It was love at first bite.

Herman and Lily have been married for so long they take each other for grunted.

LILY: Marilyn's broken up with another boyfriend!
GRANDPA: Well, he was rather fragile.

Grandpa's Mixed Brew

Did you hear about the time the Munsters' house was burgled?
The police sent along their best detective – Sherlock Bones.

The Munsters thought about moving once – to Gravesend.

LILY: Will you and your friends keep quiet?
EDDIE: But Mum, we were only ghoulling around.

How many Munsters does it take to change a light bulb?
None. They aren't afraid of the dark.

What are Munsters favourite trees?
Ceme-trees.

Did you hear about the Munsters' house at 1313 Mockingbird Lane?
It came complete with a drawbridge, dragon run, crocodile pit and an electric dungeon!

LILY: Herman, look at this corset I bought in the sales.
HERMAN: Why do you want to wear that dear?
LILY: So that I can maintain my ghoullish figure of course.

LILY: Marilyn, how much did you pay for these candlesticks?
MARILYN: £5. The candles were extra.
LILY: But that's candleless!

LONG LOST FRIEND: My, Herman, Eddie really resembles his Grandpa.
HERMAN: Yes, he's a dead ringer.

LILY TO HERMAN: I'm just off to my friend's house, dear. She's holding a coffin morning.

Did you hear about the werewolf who opened the launderette? It's called 'Wash and Werewolf'. He's opening another business soon – this time it's a Dry Screamers.

Did you hear about the questionnaire the Munsters received?
It was sent 'Tomb it may concern'.

Did you hear that Lily knitted Eddie a scarf for Christmas?
It didn't fit though – it was a bit noose.

HERMAN: What are you reading Lily?
LILY: Oh, just my horrorscope in the paper, dear.

GRANDPA: I wonder where the Dragula got that puncture?
HERMAN: Perhaps it was that last fork in the road.

Which Munster wears the biggest boots?
The one with the biggest feet.

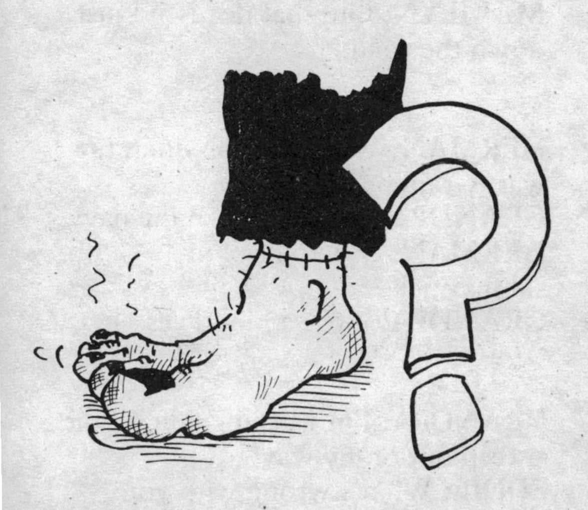

LILY: Herman, pick up your feet when you walk.
HERMAN: Why dear, I've only got to put them down again.

EDDIE: Was Great Uncle Frankenstein talented, Dad?
HERMAN: You could say he was a man of many parts.

EDDIE TO GIRL ON BUS: Do you go to the same school as Marilyn?
GIRL ON BUS: No, I go to the local ghouls school.

GRANDPA: Where does your new friend live Marilyn?
MARILYN: Oh, that dead-end just down the road.

HERMAN: What did you do in the war, Grandpa?
GRANDPA: Why, I was in the navy.
HERMAN: Did you sail in a submarine?
GRANDPA: No – a blood vessel.

GRANDPA: I'm warning you, Eddie – keep out of my way!
EDDIE: What's wrong with you Grandpa?
GRANDPA: Nothing – I just don't like being crossed.

EDDIE: Mum, where are you?
LILY: I'm in the kitchen dear. Did you have a good day at school?
EDDIE: Yes – I made a new fiend and I've brought him home to meet you.

EDDIE: What was the inscription on Great Uncle Frankenstein's tomb Dad?
HERMAN: Rust in pieces.

Where does Eddie go to school?
At the local ghoullege.

Do you know how the teacher greets the students there?
'Hello, boils and ghouls!'

His best friend, the werewolf, is always telling jokes. In fact, he wants to be a comedian when he groans up. After all, he makes people howl with laughter.

Did you hear what happened when Eddie joined the Scouts?
He scared the old ladies across the street.

Did you hear that Eddie passed all his exams? He got extinction.

EDDIE: Dad, our school is haunted!
HERMAN: Oh really, son?
EDDIE: Yes, the teachers are always going on about school spirit.

EDDIE: Grandpa, why are ghosts such cowards?
GRANDPA: Because they haven't any guts!

When Eddie was a baby, none of the family could sleep. All he did was howl all night.

Eddie's got a great sense of humour. He always loves playing the April Ghoul.

Eddie used to ride a bike to school but he had to stop. It was a vicious cycle.

EDDIE: Grandpa, you've got to help me!
GRANDPA: What's wrong?
EDDIE: I can't find my homework – all my exorcise books have vanished.

EDDIE: Mum, I've won a part in the school play!
LILY: That's great dear – what's the show?
EDDIE: We're doing a phantomime.

EDDIE: Grandpa, can you help me with my maths please?
GRANDPA: Of course. What's the problem?
EDDIE: It says here: 'How many Munsters can you cram into an empty coffin measuring 600cm × 98cm?'
GRANDPA: Well, that's easy – one. After that it isn't empty!

FIEND: What's your favourite game?
EDDIE: Haunt and seek.

Eddie loves writing music. He wants to be a decomposer when he grows up.

Did you hear about the snowman Eddie made?
It was abominable.

EDDIE: Grandpa, can you help me with my homework again?
GRANDPA: Oh Eddie, you always seem to need help. You're such a blood clot.

HERMAN: Does Eddie still believe in Father Christmas?
LILY: No, but he does believe in Santa Claws.

EDDIE: Grandpa, I fell off my bike on the way home!
GRANDPA: My goodness Eddie, how did you do that?
EDDIE: Something got caught in the spooks.

EDDIE: Grandpa, I'm in the dark about my homework.
GRANDPA: Well, turn on the light Eddie, it might help.

LILY: Eddie, do you have a form captain?
EDDIE: No, we have a spooksperson.

EDDIE: Can I play the piano, Mum?
LILY: Wash your hands first.
EDDIE: But Mum, I'll only play the black notes.

EDDIE: Grandpa, can you make a noise like a frog?
GRANDPA: Why do you ask, Eddie?
EDDIE: Well, Mum said we'll get £5,000 when you croak.

EDDIE: Mum, there's someone at the door collecting for the Old Folks' Home. Shall I give them Grandpa?

EDDIE: My best friend broke my train set!
GRANDPA: How did he do that?
EDDIE: I hit him on the head with it.

Eddie's a very keen sportsman. In fact, he's so keen you could say he's deadicated.

Eddie's taking up a new sport – skin diving.

LILY: Eddie, stop behaving so badly! Anyone would think you were a spoiled bat!